Written by Rachel Lawrence
Illustrated by Andrea Evans

First published by Parragon in 2010

Parragon
Queen Street House
4 Queen Street
Bath BA1 1HE, UK

ISBN 978-1-4075-8592-5

Printed in China

My Baby Book

PaRragon

Bath • New York • Singapore • Hong Kong • Cologne • Delhi • Melbourne

moments we don't want to forget...

this is a picture of me at.................weeks

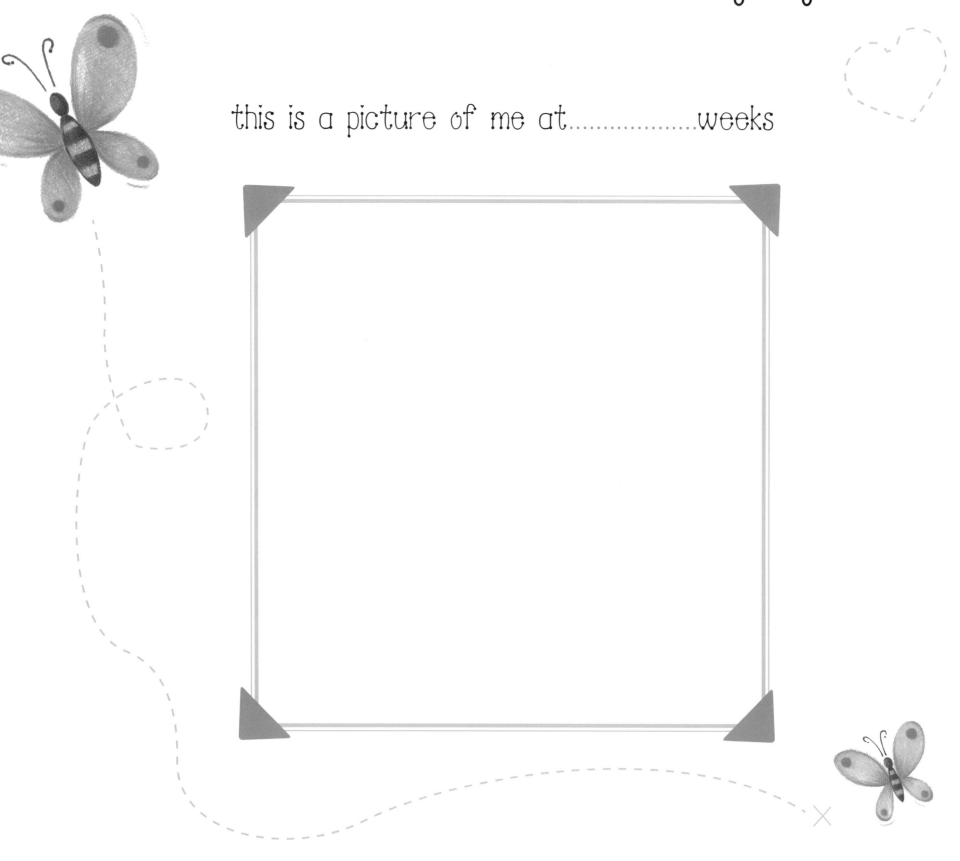

mommy's food cravings during pregnancy

how the news of my arrival was celebrated

we received the following gifts

what mommy was doing on the day I was born

mommy and daddy

mommy's name ....

mommy's birth date ....

mommy's place of birth ....

mommy's horoscope ....

mommy's hair color ....

mommy's eye color ....

mommy's job ....

mommy's hobbies ....

daddy's name ....

daddy's birth date ....

daddy's place of birth ....

daddy's horoscope ....

daddy's hair color ....

daddy's eye color ....

daddy's job ....

daddy's hobbies ....

my name

my name is ....

what my name means ....

....

the reason my name was chosen ....

....

my mommy and daddy might have called me ....

....

my family tree

great grandparents	great grandparents	great grandparents	great grandparents
....	....	....	....
....	....	....	....
grandpa	grandma	grandpa	grandma
....	....	....	....
aunts/uncles	mommy	daddy	aunts/uncles
....	....		....
....			....
....	me		....
brothers	....		sisters
....			....
....			....

my birth

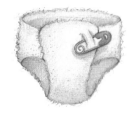

I was born on ....

at this time ....

at ....

I weighed ....

I was .... long

my hair was ....

people at the birth ....

my first visitors were ....

here is a picture of me when I was born

cute cheeks

cute nose

cute eyes

cute toes!

Rock-a-bye, Baby

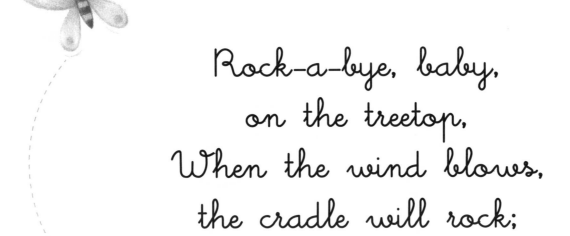

Rock-a-bye, baby,
on the treetop,
When the wind blows,
the cradle will rock;

When the bough breaks,
the cradle will fall,
Down will come baby,
cradle and all.

my first days at home

I came home on ....

I lived at ....

....

my first visitors at home ....

gifts I received ....

....

....

....

how I slept in my first week ....

how mommy and daddy felt in the first week

....

....

a photo of me in my first few days

teeny

tiny

and

totally

cute!

date taken ....

Itsy Bitsy Spider

Itsy Bitsy spider
climbing up the spout,
Down came the rain
and washed the spider out.
Out came the sun,
and dried up all the rain,
Itsy Bitsy spider
climbed up the spout again.

If You're Happy
and You Know it

If you're happy and you know it,
Clap your hands.
If you're happy and you know it,
Clap your hands.
If you're happy and you know it,
And you really want to show it,
If you're happy and you know it,
Clap your hands.

bath time

the first time I had a bath in the big bathtub

....

my favorite bath-time toys

....

here is a photo of me in the tub

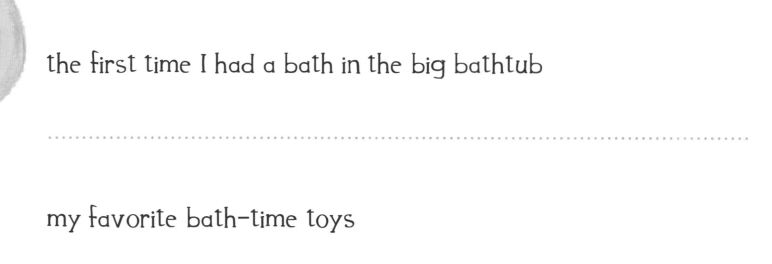

bath time
is so
much fun!

date taken

....

bedtime

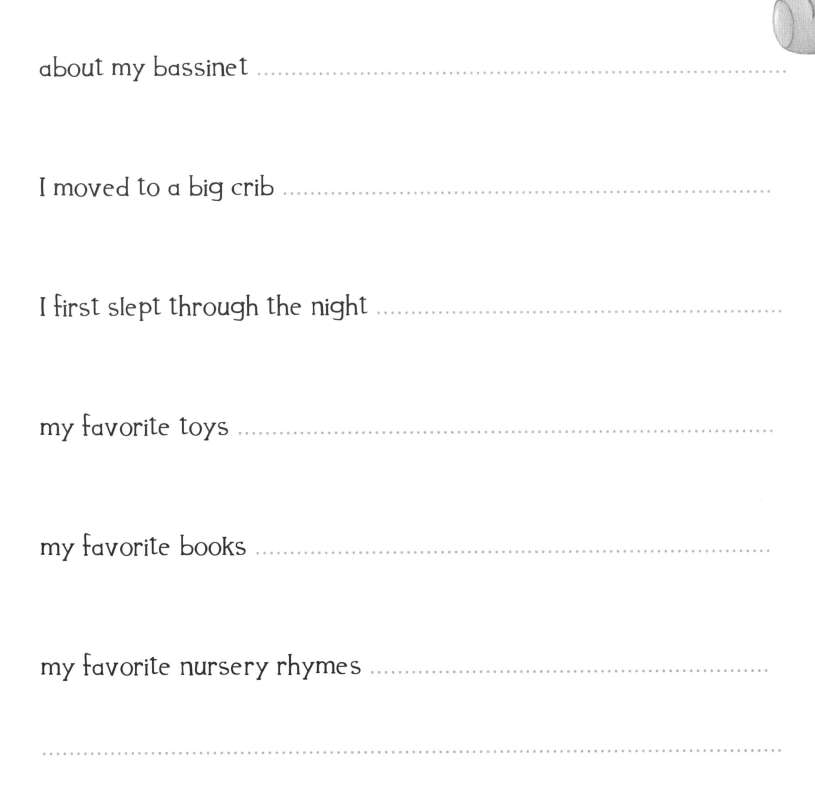

about my bassinet ....

I moved to a big crib ....

I first slept through the night ....

my favorite toys ....

my favorite books ....

my favorite nursery rhymes ....

....

Twinkle, Twinkle, Little Star

Twinkle, twinkle, little star,
How I wonder what you are!
Up above the world so high,
Like a diamond in the sky.

When the blazing sun is gone,
When he nothing shines upon,
Then you show your little light,
Twinkle, twinkle all the night.

Then the traveler in the dark—
Thanks you for your tiny spark,
He could not see which way to go,
If you did not twinkle so.

In the dark blue sky you keep,
And often through my curtains peep,
For you never shut your eye,
'Till the sun is in the sky.

As your bright and tiny spark,
Lights the traveler in the dark—
Though I know not what you are,
Twinkle, twinkle, little star.

Jane Taylor

my footprint

date taken ....

my handprint

date taken ....

 I'm so new!

Jack and Jill

Jack and Jill went up the hill,
To fetch a pail of water;
Jack fell down and broke his crown,
And Jill came tumbling after.

Then Jack got up, and home did trot,
As fast as he could caper;
He went to bed, to mend his head,
With vinegar and brown paper.

first moves

I first rolled over ....

I sat up all by myself ....

I crawled ....

I took my very first steps ....

a photo of me
on the move

look who's
crawling!

date taken

....

first food

first food ....

I first drank from a cup ....

favorite fruit purees ....

foods I like ....

foods I dislike ....

my special treats ....

I first sat in a high chair ....

Lavender's Blue

Lavender's blue, dilly, dilly,
Lavender's green;
When I am king, dilly, dilly,
You shall be queen.

Hey Diddle Diddle

Hey diddle diddle, the cat and the fiddle,
The cow jumped over the moon.
The little dog laughed to see such fun,
And the dish ran away with the spoon!

 first trips and outings

my first outing on a train or bus ....

my first vacation or trip was to ....

what I loved ....

what I didn't like ....

here is a photo of me on my vacation

date taken ....

bon voyage!

Hickory Dickory Dock

Hickory dickory dock,
The mouse ran up the clock.
The clock struck one,
The mouse ran down,
Hickory dickory dock.

Ring Around the Rosy

Ring around the rosy,
A pocket full of posies.
Ashes! Ashes!
We all fall down.

1 month

things I can do now ....

....

funny things I do ....

....

how I've been sleeping ....

....

I weigh ....

I'm .... long

this is me at one month

this is me and my family

it runs in
the family

2 months

new things I can do ....

....

funny sounds I make ....

....

I smile when ....

my favorite nursery rhymes ....

....

I weigh ....

I'm .... long

I'm awake
a lot more
now!

here I am at two months

 tiny yawns and sleepy sighs,
nursery rhymes and lullabies.

Humpty Dumpty

Humpty Dumpty sat on a wall,
Humpty Dumpty had a great fall;
All the king's horses, and all the king's men
Couldn't put Humpty together again!

Rain, Rain, Go Away

Rain, rain, go away,
Come again another day.
Little Jenny wants to play.

 **months**

things I can do ....

....

I love these toys and games ....

....

funny things I do ....

....

I weigh ....

I am .... long

this is me at three months

 growing cuter
by the day!

 **months**

I like toys that make loud noises!

new things I can do now ....

....

baby groups I go to ....

....

new places I've been to ....

....

I weigh ....

I am .... long

this is me at four months

this is a photo of me sleeping

snug as
a bug in
a hug!

Little Miss Muffet

Little Miss Muffet
Sat on a tuffet,
Eating her curds and whey;
Along came a spider,
Who sat down beside her
And frightened Miss Muffet away.

Row, Row, Row Your Boat

Row, row, row your boat
Gently down the stream.
Merrily, merrily, merrily, merrily,
Life is but a dream.

 months

things I can do at five months ....

....

funny things I do ....

....

my favorite things to hug ....

....

I weigh ....

I am .... long

I love bouncing up and down!

here I am at five months!

 a new little
hand to hold

6 months

My favorite game is "peek-a-boo"

new things I can do ....

....

favorite bathtime toys ....

....

how I've been sleeping ....

....

my friends ....

I weigh ....

I am .... long

I'm six months old now!

cute as
a button

This Little Piggy

(Pretend each of the child's
toes is a little piggy.
Begin with the biggest toe and finish
by tickling under the child's foot.)

This little piggy went to market,
This little piggy stayed home,
This little piggy had roast beef,
This little piggy had none,
And this little piggy cried,
"Wee, wee, wee!"
All the way home.

 **7** months

new things I can do ....

....

my favorite toys ....

....

places I've been to ....

....

I weigh ....

I'm .... long

I love pop-up toys and other surprises!

this is me at seven months

this is a photo of me with my favorite toy

kisses and
hugs
sent from
above

 **months**

I can pick things up now!

new things I can do ....

....

my friends are ....

....

my favorite toy/book is ....

....

I weigh ....

I am .... long

a photo of me at eight months

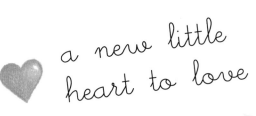
a new little
heart to love

Little Bo-Peep

Little Bo-Peep has lost her sheep,
And doesn't know where to find them;
Leave them alone,
and they'll come home,
Wagging their tails behind them.

Mary Had a Little Lamb

Mary had a little lamb,
Its fleece was white as snow;
And everywhere that Mary went
The lamb was sure to go.
It followed her to school one day,
Which was against the rule;
It made the children laugh and play
To see a lamb at school.

 **months**

new things I can do ....

....

cute things I do ....

....

new foods I've eaten ....

....

I weigh ....

I am .... long

I love building blocks!

this is me at nine months!

 growing cuter
by the day

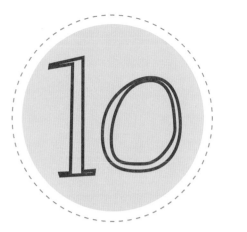 **10** months

things I can do at 10 months ....

....

my favorite activity ....

....

words I understand ....

....

foods I like ....

I weigh ....

I am .... long

this is me at ten months

this is a photo of me being a messy eater!

little arms to hold tight, little cheeks to kiss good night!

# Five Little Ducks

Five little ducks went swimming one day,
Over the hills and far away.
Mother Duck said, "Quack, quack, quack, quack,"
But only four little ducks came back.

Four little ducks went swimming one day,
Over the hills and far away.
Mother Duck said, "Quack, quack, quack, quack,"
But only three little ducks came back.

Three little ducks went swimming one day,
Over the hills and far away.
Mother Duck said, "Quack, quack, quack, quack,"
But only two little ducks came back.

Two little ducks went swimming one day,
Over the hills and far away.
Mother Duck said, "Quack, quack, quack, quack,"
But only one little duck came back.

One little duck went swimming one day,
Over the hills and far away.
Mother Duck said, "Quack, quack, quack, quack,"
But none of the five little ducks came back.

Mother Duck went swimming one day,
Over the hills and far away.
Mother Duck said, "Quack, quack, quack, quack,"
And five little ducks came swimming back.

 **11** months

new things I can do ....

....

my favorite first words ....

....

I have .... teeth

I weigh ....

I'm .... long

I'm getting mobile!

I'm eleven months old!

here I am on the move

sweetness is
hereditary

12 months

I can say my first words!

new things I can do ....

....

words I can say now ....

....

funny things I do ....

....

I weigh ....

I am .... long

a photo of me at twelve months

 it's the little things
that matter most

my first birthday

what I did ....

....

who came to see me ....

....

gifts I received ....

happy
1st birthday

....

food I ate ....

my first Christmas

I spent the day with ....

....

I received these gifts ....

....

the best parts of the day were ....

....

food I ate ....

this is me on my first Christmas day!

date taken ....

Sing a Song of Sixpence

Sing a song of sixpence
A pocket full of rye;
Four and twenty blackbirds
Baked in a pie.
When the pie was opened
The birds began to sing;
Now wasn't that a dainty dish
To set before the king?

The king was in his counting house,
Counting out his money;
The queen was in the parlor
Eating bread and honey.
The maid was in the garden,
Hanging out the clothes,
When down came a blackbird
And pecked off her nose!

The Queen of Hearts

The Queen of Hearts, she made some tarts,
All on a summer's day.
The Knave of Hearts, he stole the tarts,
And took them clean away.

The King of Hearts, called for the tarts,
And beat the Knave full sore.
The Knave of Hearts, brought back the tarts
And vowed he'd steal no more.

my naming day

I spent the day with ....

....

gifts I received ....

....

....

the best parts of the day were ....

....

....

this is me on my naming day

date taken ....

One, Two, Buckle my Shoe

One, two, buckle my shoe;

Three, four, knock at the door;

Five, six, pick up sticks;

Seven, eight, lay them straight;

Nine, ten, a big fat hen;

Eleven, twelve, dig and delve;

Thirteen, fourteen, maids a-courting;

Fifteen, sixteen, maids in the kitchen;

Seventeen, eighteen, maids in waiting;

Nineteen, twenty, my plate's empty!

visits to the doctor

my pediatrician is ....

....

....

immunizations ....

....

....

....

....

....

....

....

allergies ....

....

....

....

illnesses ....

....

....

....

....

....

Round and Round the Garden

Round and round the garden,
Round and round the garden
Like a teddy bear;
(Draw a circle on the palm of your
baby's hand with your finger)

One step, two steps,
(Walk your fingers up your baby's arm)

Tickle you under there!
(Tickle baby under the arm)

Teddy Bear, Teddy Bear

Teddy bear, teddy bear,
Touch the ground.
Teddy bear, teddy bear,
Turn around.

Teddy bear, teddy bear,
Walk upstairs.
Teddy bear, teddy bear,
Say your prayers.

Teddy bear, teddy bear,
Turn out the light.
Teddy bear, teddy bear,
Say goodnight.

a year in pictures

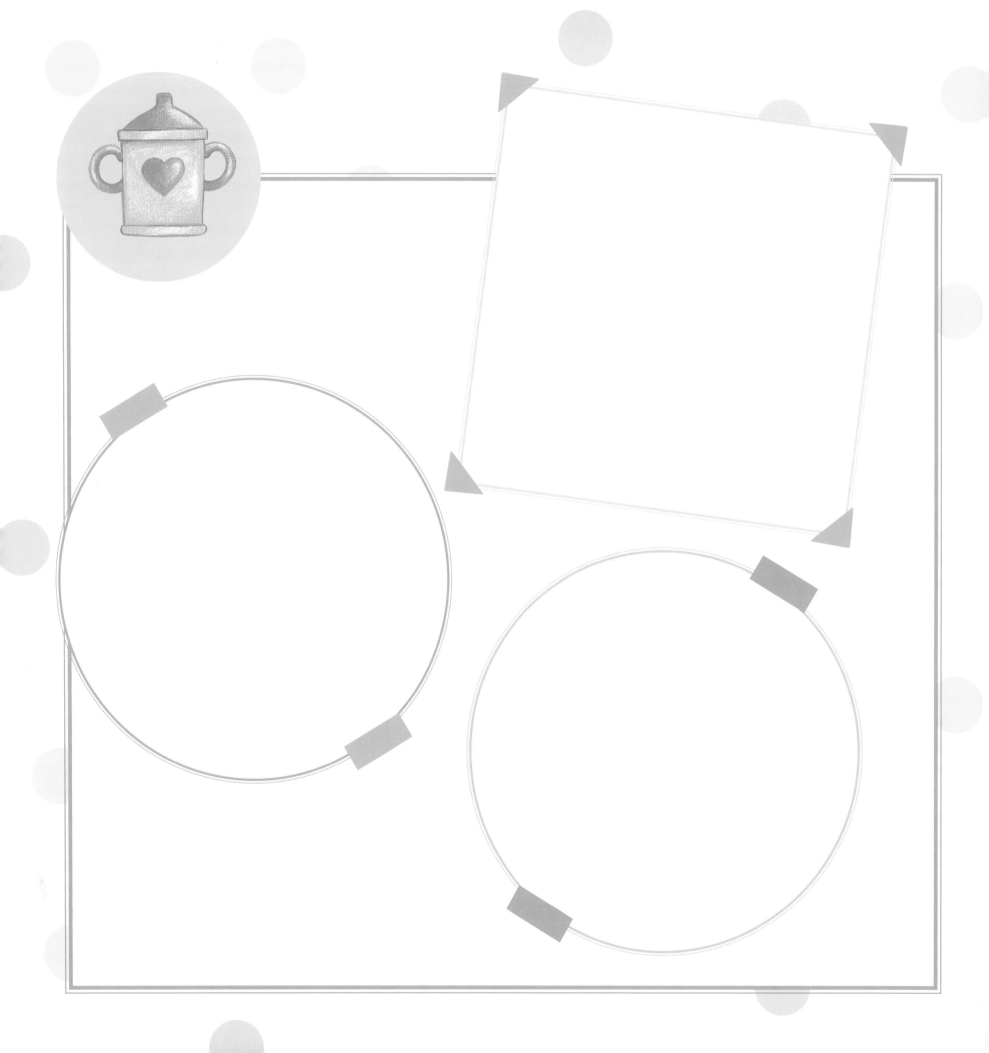

other special things about me...